Budgeting and Spending Skills 1
Activity Book

by

Marna A. Owen

Marjorie L. Kelley, Ed.D.

Director of Education

Yong Situ

Illustrator

Quercus
A Division of Globe Book Company
Englewood Cliffs, New Jersey 07632

Cover Design: Graphic Media Communications

(Formerly Consumer Skills for Teenagers Activity Book ISBN 1-55555-009-6)

Printed in the United States of America
10 9 8 7 6 5 4 3 2 1
ISBN 1-55675-791-3

Consumer Skills for Teenagers Activity Book

NOTE: New title for this teacher's guide is
BUDGETING & SPENDING SKILL I
ACTIVITY BOOK TEACHER'S GUIDE (#1441)

Teacher's Guide

The *Consumers Skills for Teenagers Activity Book* is a collection of activities which extend and reinforce the concepts and vocabulary taught in the *Consumer Skills for Teenagers* text, and provide the students with further practice in various consumer skills. Clear directions allow most students to complete the activities without teacher guidance. The *Consumer Skills for Teenagers Activity Book* is written at the Spache reading level of 2.3.

How to Use the Activity Book

The chapter headings in the *Consumer Skills for Teenagers Activity Book* correspond to the chapter headings in the *Consumer Skills for Teenagers* text. In the left-hand margin of certain pages are graphic indicators. These direct the students to complete activities after reading through certain pages in the text. For example,

after page
5

indicates that the students should complete the subsequent activities after reading through page 5 in the text.

Unfamiliar Words and Answer Key

Unfamiliar words (words not on the Spache reading list) are listed by chapter. It is recommended that unfamiliar words be introduced by the teacher prior to independent work activities to maximize student success. Many of the words will already have been introduced and taught in the *Consumer Skills for Teenagers* text.

Answers are also listed for each chapter. Due to the subjective nature of most exercises (self assessment, etc.) many of the answers and results will vary among the students. These are so noted.

Introduction *Unfamiliar words:* text, skills, labels, activities, consumers, page.

1: Consumer Skills *Unfamiliar words:* services, records, life, write, below, teenagers, peanuts, movie theaters, sports teams, yourself, sentence, check, enjoyed, add, subtract, decimal points.

page answers
5 records, singers; race cars, driver; footballs, football players; TV shows, TV stars; books, teachers; potatoes, fast food cooks. **Goods and Services in Your Life:** Goods - cake, peanuts, airplane; Services - salesperson, waiter, gardener.
6 Answers will vary.
7 Answers will vary.
8 (From left to right) $.10; $30.00; $3.00; $9.50; $99.00.
9 (From left to right) $10.00; $.50; $12.00; $9.64; $5.00.

2: The Saving and Spending Plan *Unfamiliar words:* income, check, lump sums, regular, amount, multiply, percent, favorite, questions, total.

page answers
10 Answers will vary.
11 Answers will vary. **Using a Table to Check Percent:** $.25; $25.00; $12.50; $3.75; answers will vary.
12 $25.00; answers will vary.
13 Answers will vary.

3: Spending Skills *Unfamiliar words:* price, quality, trade-off, brand, features, ads, puzzle.

page answers
14 See puzzle.

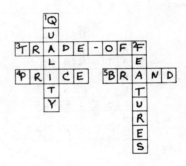

15 both the same; Quickland; Fastway; answers will vary.
16 both the same; Spring Flower; End of the Year; answers will vary.
17 Answers will vary; both the same; Summer brand; answers will vary.

4: Using Ads *Unfamiliar words:* skin, body, magazines, bait and switch, government, agencies, state, attorney general's office, post office.

page answers
18 CLEARALL; nothing; nothing; nothing; nothing; nothing; answers will vary.
19 Fierce brand; nothing; nothing; $24.99; Body Fitness; before May 4th; answers will vary.
20 Ad promises beauty. More teens use CLEARALL than any other skin cream; ad shows a well-known person using or talking about the good or service. Ad promises beauty.
21 Answers will vary.
23 U.S. Postal Service; Federal Trade Commission; state attorney general's office; answers will vary.

Quercus Corporation
2405 Castro Valley Boulevard
Castro Valley, CA 94546
(415) 886-6176
From outside California: (800) 634-3600.

5: Reading Labels *Unfamiliar words:* pa[...]ed, nutrients, serving size, calories, vitamins, percent, RDA, protein, carbohydrates, answers, ingredients, USDA, sodium, synthetic, chemicals, healthy.

page answers

24 Answers will vary.

25 Answers will vary.

26 ingredients: the things which go into a good (such as food); USDA: a government agency that gives meat and other foods the "okay"; sodium: another name for salt; nutrients: things people need to stay healthy; synthetic: cloth made from chemicals. See puzzle.

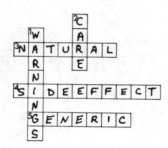

27 See puzzle.

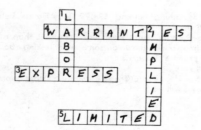

28 Answers will vary.

29 Answers will vary.

6: More Ways to Check Quality *Unfamiliar words:* warranty, registration, address, zip code, date, camera, model number, serial number, match.

page answers

34 Students fill in Figure 4 with own name, address, and date. Model number: X123; Serial number: 1278964118.

36 See puzzle.

```
      ¹L
    ⁴W A R R A N T ²I E S
      B                 M
      ³E X P R E S S     P
      O                 L
                        I
                        E
            ⁵L I M I T E D
```

37 1/2 inch; Smile; yes; Bright.

7: Getting a Good Price *Unfamiliar words:* unit pricing, ounces, grams, divide, generic, weight, boutique, factory outlet, department store.

page answers

38 pounds; $.50.

39 $1.60, 4, $.40; .50, .40, Wolf River.

40 $1.20, 60, $.2; $3.00, 150, $.2; $2.00, 200, $.1; $.2, $.2, $.1, third.

41 Figure 6; $.75, 75, $.1; $1.00, 50, $.2; Figure 6.

42 boutique: a small clothing store with high prices; factory outlet: a place to buy clothes left over after boutiques and department stores buy what they want; department store: large store with many goods, prices usually less than a boutique's; sale: a time when stores lower the prices on goods. See scramble.

```
A I S W D N N I T I S W L G C N T
A L N E T H E G D N E A E O E O Y
A C W O N E R B O U T I Q U E T H
A I H O S I E C R V E R A K P E N
L D E P A R T M E N T S T O R E O
E S O W L D L O V O I F Y N A E S
D N O W E O Y I A M D I O P N I B
R W H A T T O U G D O N A T C V T
H Y Z F A C T O R Y O U T L E T I
G N D D Q Y R N O I T I S X W A N
```

8: Three Ways to Pay for Goods and Services *Unfamiliar words:* cash, layaway, credit, receipt.

page answers

43 See puzzle.

```
            ¹L
            A
    ³M O N E Y O ²R D E R
            A     E
            W   ⁴C A S H
            A     E
            Y     I
                  P
        ⁵C R E D I T
```

9: Consumer Rights and Resources *Unfamiliar words:* sweater, information.

page answers

45 Students do role playing exercise; 5; answers will vary.

47 Students write letter using information given in exercise and Figure 8 on page 47.

10: Using What You Know

page answers

48 I would read the want ads for used cars; I would get someone who knows about cars to look at it; I would ask my friends which cars they think have good quality; I would buy a car with a good warranty.

Contents

Introduction

In the *Consumer Skills for Teenagers* text, you are learning some skills. You are learning how to save, spend, shop, read labels, and so on.

The activities in this book build on the skills taught in the *Consumer Skills for Teenagers* text. The activities build on words and facts consumers should know. In some of the activities you will put your skills to work.

Use the *Activity Book* in this way. Some pages have special words on them. These words can be found on the top-left side of some pages. These words might look like this:

after page

5

These words tell you to work in the *Activity Book* only after reading through page 5 in your text. If the words say:

after page

10

then work in the *Activity Book* only after reading through page 10 in the text, and so on.

1
Consumer Skills

after page

5

Goods and Services Together

In Chapter 1 you read about **goods** and **services.** Goods and services go together. The bus driver cannot do a service without a bus. The clothes you wear come from a clothes company. The people in that company make clothes as a service.

Below are two groups of words. On one side are goods. On the other side are people who do services. Draw a line from each good to the person who might use the good while doing a service. The first one is done for you.

Goods	People Who Do Services
glasses	TV stars
records	football players
race cars	teachers
footballs	fast food cooks
TV shows	eye doctors
books	drivers
potatoes	singers

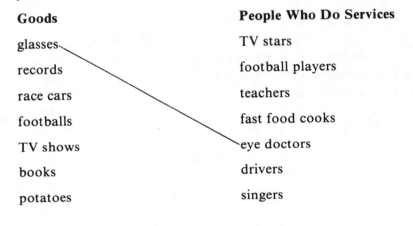

Goods and Services in Your Life

On the lines below write two other goods teenagers might buy. Then write two service jobs teenagers might get. Use the words from the list below to help you.

cake   salesperson   peanuts   airplane   waiter   gardener

Goods   **Service Jobs**

_____   _____

_____   _____

Who Is Selling to Teenage Consumers?

You read that many sellers want money from teenage consumers. Which sellers in your city are trying to sell to teenagers? To find out, do the following.

Think about shops in your city. Which shops sell clothes that you like to wear? Which shops sell music you like? Which shops sell things you like to hang in your room? Write the names of three of the shops.

_____

_____

_____

Where do you and your friends go on the weekends? Where do you go after school (after homework is finished, of course)? Are there special food places, movie theaters, or sports teams you go to see? Write the names of three of the places.

_____

_____

_____

Name the place where you spend most of your money.

_____

Know Yourself

See how well you know yourself. Below is the beginning of a sentence: *It is most important to me . . .* The sentence can be finished in three ways. Check (✓) the sentence which tells how you feel. Check only one way to finish each sentence.

It is most important to me . . .

_____ to buy clothes that look like my friends' clothes.

_____ to wear clothes that look best on me.

_____ to wear clothes that feel good.

It is most important to me . . .

_____ to spend my money on things that will last.

_____ to spend my money on my friends.

_____ to spend my money on things that can only be enjoyed a short while.

It is most important to me . . .

_____ to save money for what I want in the years ahead.

_____ to save money for things I want right now.

_____ to spend all my money and save none of it.

It is most important to me . . .

_____ to buy food that tastes good.

_____ to buy food that is good for me.

_____ to buy food that doesn't cost a lot.

Do you know yourself very well? Knowing yourself is a skill. It may be that you are spending your money in ways that are not important to you. If so, you may want to make a plan to change. Buy the goods and services you really want. Then you will be making the best use of your money.

Getting Ready for Saving and Spending Plans

In Chapter 2 you will learn about saving and spending plans. You will need to add and subtract dollars and cents. The next two pages will help you remember what you know about adding and subtracting money.

What is special about numbers that show dollars and cents? They usually have **decimal points (.).** Dollars are on the left of the decimal point. Cents are on the right of the decimal point. It is important to "line up" the decimal points before doing a problem. Look at the following problem:

Suppose you want to add $5.00 and .35. To do so, you would write:

$$\begin{array}{r} \$5.00 \\ +\ \ .35 \\ \hline \$5.35 \end{array}$$

Notice that the decimal points (.) are in line. One is directly below the other. Now here is one wrong way to write the same problem:

$$\begin{array}{r} \$5.00 \\ +\ .35 \\ \hline \end{array}$$

Lining up the decimal points is important. This is true for adding and subtracting dollars and cents. This will help you do the problems in the right way.

Make It Right

Below are some problems with dollars and cents. The decimal points are not in line. Write the problems under the heading **"Right Way."** Put the decimal points in line. Then find the answers to the problems. Don't forget to put a dollar sign ($) by each of your answers. The first one is done for you.

Wrong Way	Right Way	Wrong Way	Right Way
$6.50 − .50	$\begin{array}{r} \$6.50 \\ -\ \ \ .50 \\ \hline \$6.00 \end{array}$	$ .55 −.45	
$10.00 + 20.00		$1.50 + 1.50	
$18.50 − 9.00		$100.00 − 1.00	

More Practice

Now write and do the following problems. Some numbers you will add. Some numbers you will subtract. Make sure the decimal points are in line in both kinds of problems. Remember to put a dollar sign by your answers. The first one is done for you.

Add $5.00 and $3.55.   Subtract $10.00 from $20.00.

$$\begin{array}{r} \$5.00 \\ +\ 3.55 \\ \hline \$8.55 \end{array}$$

Subtract $.50 from $1.00.   Add $6.00 and $6.00.

Add $8.99 and $.65.   Subtract $5.00 from $10.00.

2
The Saving and Spending Plan

after page

9

How Do You Get Your Income?

Read through the following sentences. Check (✓) the sentences that are true for you. Then fill in the lines that follow the sentences you have checked. Some words are given to help you. Use other words if you need to. Do not fill in the lines that are not true for you.

_____ I get income in lump sums. (Check if true.)

The last lump sum I got was for $ _____ . I got it

_____ .

(for a holiday/for my birthday/for working/to buy something special)

The next lump sum I might get could be

_____ .

(for a holiday/for my birthday/for working/to buy something special)

_____ I get regular income. (Check if true.)

Each _____

(day/week/two weeks/month)

I get $ _____ . I get this regular income

from my _____

(job/parents)

_____ Someday soon I plan to get regular income. (Check if true.) I would

like to get a job doing _____ .

I think I can make $ _____ an hour.

Amount of Inco
$ 1.00
5.00
10.00
15.00
20.00
25.00
30.00
35.00
40.00
45.00
50.00
55.00
60.00
65.00
70.00
75.00
80.00
85.00
90.00
95.00
100.00
500.00

Figure 1. Table for Fi

Saving Part of Your Income

Now pick one amount of income you wrote on page 10. You can pick an amount you once had, have now, or will have. Write this amount on the line next to the word "Income" below.

You should save at least 25% of that income when you get it. Multiply that income by .25 to find how much you should save. Do the problem. Then write your answer next to the word "Savings" below.

Income: _____

x   .25   _____

Savings: $ _____

% of Income
$ .25
1.25
2.50
3.75
5.00
6.25
7.50
8.75
10.00
11.25
12.50
13.75
15.00
16.25
17.50
18.75
20.00
21.25
22.50
23.75
25.00
125.00

25% of Some Amounts

Using a Table to Check Percent

Figure 1 is a table. It can help you find what is 25% of certain amounts of money. This is how to use the table. Look under the words "Amount of Income" on the left side of the table. Find "$1.00." What is the number directly across from it? Write the answer below.

_____

If you wrote $.25, you are right. 25% of $1.00 is $.25. Now write the answers to the following problems.

What is 25% of $100.00? $ _____

What is 25% of $50.00? $ _____

What is 25% of $15.00? $ _____

Look at the amount of income you wrote at the top of the page. Which

amount of income on Figure 1 is closest to it? $ _____

What is 25% of that amount? $ _____

What Would You Do With $100.00?

There is a favorite question that friends like to ask each other. "What would you do with a million dollars?" they ask with stars in their eyes. You could do a lot. In this activity you will not get a million dollars. You will imagine you have a lump sum income of $100.00.

First you would save 25% of your income. You could multiply $100.00 by .25 to find 25%. You could also look at the table on page 11. When you find the answer, fill in the lines below.

25% of $100.00 is _____ .

Now how much money do you have left to spend? Subtract your savings from your income.

Income: $100.00

Savings: -_____

Total spending money: _____

Suppose there is nothing you *must* spend your money on. Make a list of three things to spend your money on. Write as closely as you can what each good or service will cost. Put the list in order. Put the things you want most on the top of the list.

What I Want	What It Costs
1.	
2.	
3.	

Do you have enough money to buy everything on the list? Write *yes* or *no.*

_____

Do you have enough money to buy the thing that is most important to you? Write *yes* or *no.*

_____

How would you choose to spend your money? Circle the number of the thing on your list that you would buy. (You can also choose to save your money. If you would like to do this, don't circle any of the numbers.)

Making Your Own Plan

Look at Figure 2. It is a saving and spending plan. In this activity you will fill in Figure 2. You can use your own income. What if you do not have any income? Use a lump sum income of $50.00. Do the same steps you followed on page 12. Go back and read Chapter 2 in the text again if you need to. Remember to use the table on page 11 of this book for help on percent.

Income: _____
(lump sum or
regular income)

Savings: - _____

Total spending money: _____

Things I must spend for: What they cost:

_____   _____

_____   _____

_____ + _____

Amount I must spend: _____

Total spending money: _____

Amount I must spend: _____

Money left for other
things I want: _____

Figure 2. Your Saving and Spending Plan

3
Spending Skills

after page

20

Words For Consumers

Look at the list of words. Use them to fill in the sentences below. You can find the words and their meanings in Chapter 3 of the text.

price   quality   trade-off   brand   features   ads

Down

1. John wanted his shoes to last. He wanted them to have good

_____ .

2. The shoes had to be white and made of cloth. These were two

_____ he was looking for.

Across

3. John finally found a pair of shoes that had good quality. But they were

blue. John would have to _____ - _____ a

feature to get quality.

4. John had to make sure he found a pair of shoes under $40.00. This was

the highest _____ he could pay.

5. Each _____ of shoes had different features, prices, and quality.

Now use the above words and the directions to fill in the puzzle.

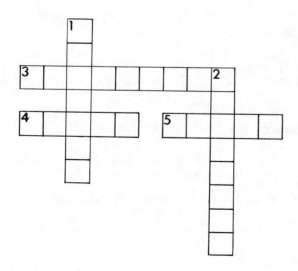

What Would You Trade-Off?

Sometimes you cannot find the perfect good or service. Sometimes you must give up some of one thing to get more of another. This is called a trade-off. You will be making trade-offs on pages 15-17. On each page is a table. It tells you the features, quality, and prices of goods or services. Read through each table. Then pick and write the answers to the questions.

	Fastway breakfast	**Quickland breakfast**
Features	eggs, potatoes, bread, large orange drink	eggs, potatoes, small orange drink
Quality	sometimes cold when you get it	always fresh and hot when you get it
Price	$3.80	$3.80

Imagine you have $5.00 to spend on breakfast. You can get your breakfast at Fastway or Quickland.

Which breakfast costs less?

_____

Fastway/Quickland/both the same

Which food place has better quality food?

_____

Fastway/Quickland/both the same

Which food place gives you more food (features) for $3.80?

_____

Fastway/Quickland/both the same

I would have breakfast at _____.
                                      Fastway/Quickland

I would trade-off _____
                      some features/some quality

to get _____.
      better features/better quality

	Spring Flower Dance	**End of the Year Dance**
Features	live band, big dance floor, food	live band, food, big dance floor
Quality	both band and food are very good	band and food are just "okay"
Price	$7.00 per person	$4.00 per person

Imagine you have $15.00 to take your friend dancing. There are two dances coming up. The Spring Flower Dance and the End of the Year Dance.

Which dance has better features?

_____

Spring Flower/End of the Year/both the same

Which dance has the better quality band and food?

_____

Spring Flower/End of the Year/both the same

Which dance costs less money?

_____

Spring Flower/End of the Year/both the same

I would take my friend to the _____

_____.

Spring Flower Dance/End of the Year Dance

I would trade-off some _____
       quality/some money

to get _____.
  better quality/a better price

	Summer brand pants	**Turtle brand pants**
Features	white and light, cut makes you look fat, wash and wear	white, but cloth is heavy, cut makes you look thin, wash and wear
Quality	made well, can be returned	made well, can be returned
Price	$35.00	$45.00

Imagine you have $45.00 to spend on some new pants. But you would really like to spend less on the pants than $45.00. You would like some white pants. They should be made of light cloth. You look at Summer brand pants and Turtle brand pants.

Which pair of pants has the features you most want?

_____

Turtle brand/Summer brand/both the same

Which pair of pants has better quality?

_____

Turtle brand/Summer brand/both the same

Which pair of pants costs less?

_____

Turtle brand/Summer brand/both the same

I would buy _____ .
         Turtle brand pants/Summer brand pants

I would trade-off _____
                  features/some money

to get _____ .
       more features/a better price

4
Using Ads

after page
24

Ask Yourself These Questions About Ads

Look at the ad on this page. Read through it.

Beautiful Skin —
Beautiful You.

Take Away Those
Ugly Spots With
CLEARALL!

CLEARALL

More teens use CLEARALL
than any other skin cream.

On the lines below, write the answers to the following questions. They are questions that skillful consumers should always ask about ads.

• What is the ad telling me about the good? (The ad may not tell you anything about some of the things below. If this is so, write the word *nothing*.)

brand name _____

quality _____

features _____

price _____

where to buy _____

when to buy _____

• Do I believe the ad? (Write *yes* or *no*.) _____

• Do I need what the ad is trying to make me buy?

(Write *yes* or *no*. _____)

18

Look at the ad on this page. Read through it.

Look Your Best With

FIERCE BRAND

Body Building Food Plan

Used by
Jack "The Giant" Smith
World Class Body Builder

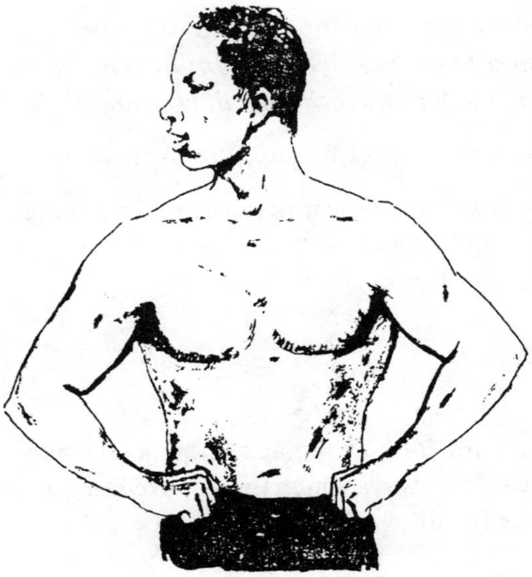

Now on Sale
$24.00
At All
Body Fitness Stores

Offer good until May 4th

On the lines below, write the answers to the following questions.

• What is the ad telling me about the good or service? (The ad may not tell about some of the things below. If that is so, write the word *nothing*.)

brand name _____

features _____

quality _____

price _____

where to buy _____

when to buy _____

• Do I believe the ad? (Write *yes* or *no*.) _____

• Do I really want what the ad is trying to make me buy?

(Write *yes* or *no*.) _____

How Do Ads Make Consumers Want to Buy Goods and Services?

Ads try to get consumers to buy a good or a service. Ads have special ways of doing this. Read through the list below.

• Ad shows a well-known person using or talking about the good or service.

• Ad shows how a good or service works.

• Ad says that one brand of a good or a service was liked more than another brand. *"Seven out of ten people liked Elephant brand peanuts more than the other leading brand."*

• Ad promises beauty, fun, or love.

• Ad makes consumers afraid something bad will happen if they don't use a good or service.

Now look at the ads on pages 18 and 19 in this book again. Write at least two ways which the ads used to get consumers to buy something. Use the list above to help you.

Ad for Skin Cream

_____

_____

_____

_____

_____

Ad for Body Building Plan

_____

_____

_____

_____

_____

Are You Being Followed by Ads?

In the *Consumer Skills for Teenagers* text, you read about Jerry. He saw that ads were all around him. He felt like someone was always trying to sell him something.

Are you being followed by ads? For the next two days, make it a point to look at ads. Listen to them on the radio. Read signs along the road. Look in teen magazines or newspapers. Watch TV.

Find three ads. Then fill in the lines below. Write what the ad was selling (brand name). Then write one way that the ad used to get the consumer to buy the good or service. Use the list on page 20 to help you.

What the Ad Was Selling   **One Way the Ad Used to Get Consumers to Buy**

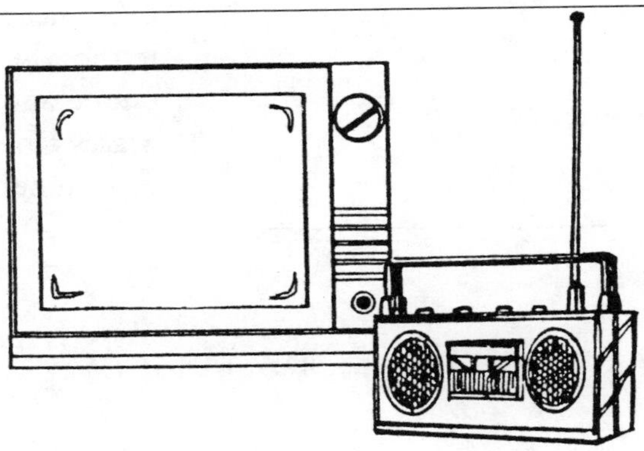

_____

_____

_____

_____

_____

_____

_____

_____

_____

_____

_____

_____

What You Can Do About Untruthful Ads

All ads are not truthful. You know about **bait and switch.** You know that mail order ads are not always truthful.

What can consumers do about untruthful advertising? Some government agencies try to stop untruthful advertising. It is up to consumers to tell the agencies about the untruthful ads. In some cases, the agencies can help consumers get back the money they lost because of the ads. Figure 3 shows these agencies and where to find them. Use Figure 3 to answer the questions on page 23.

What Kind of Ad	Agency to Call	Where to Find Them
Any ad which is seen in more than one state	Federal Trade Commission (FTC)	Bureau of Consumer Protection Federal Trade Commission, Washington, D.C. 20580 202-523-3727
Ads which are shown only in your state or city	State attorney general's office	Look in the white pages of your phone book under your state name. Or look under **Consumer Complaints/False or Deceptive Advertising.**
Ads for mail order	U.S. Postal Service	Go to or call the post office nearest you. Look in the white pages of your phone book under **United States Government.** Then look under **Postal Service.**

Figure 3.   Where to Find Help

You saw an ad for a "Wonder Box." A company would mail you a box full of things to make you beautiful. First you had to mail the company $3.99. The company would send the box in 30 days. You sent in your money. Two months have gone by. The company has still not sent you the good. You wrote the company one letter. They never answered. You tried to call them. Their phone number was no longer working.

You have never had problems with mail order before. What agency could you go to for help?

_____

There was an ad on TV that was selling mouthwash. The ad said the mouthwash would take away bad breath. You tried the mouthwash after eating something that smelled strong. Then you went out with a friend. Your friend said your breath smelled, then went home early. You called the company. You told them the mouthwash did not work. They just laughed.

The ad was shown all over the country. What agency could you go to for help?

_____

A small clothes store in your town had an ad on the radio. The ad said the store would give you a free hat on Saturday. You went to the store on Saturday. The salesperson said you had to buy something. Then you could get the hat. The ad had not said that. You talked to the person who ran the store. He didn't listen.

The clothes store has ads only in your state. What agency could you go to for help?

_____

What is the phone number of the post office nearest you? Use the directions on Figure 3 to help you find it. Then write it on the line below.

_____

Now find the phone number to call if you have a problem with an ad in your state. Use the directions in Figure 3 to help you find it. Write the phone number on the line below.

_____

5
Reading Labels

after page
30

What's That You're Eating?

Do you ever eat packaged foods? Chances are you do. Bread, candy, and milk are packaged. So are many other things that are brought in stores.

Look through your kitchen at home. Find two packaged foods which list nutrients on their labels. Read the label on the first food. Then fill out the lines on this page. Then look at the second packaged food. Use it to fill out the lines on page 25.

Packaged Food Number One

Food _____ Brand _____

What is the serving size? _____

What is the number of calories in each serving?

_____

List the vitamins in the food. Give the percent (%) of the RDA in each serving.

_____

_____

_____

_____

Is there any protein in a serving? Write *yes* or *no*.

_____

Is there any fat in a serving? Write *yes* or *no*.

_____

Are there any carbohydrates in a serving? Write *yes* or *no*.

_____

Packaged Food Number Two

Food _____ Brand _____

What is the serving size? _____

What is the number of calories in each serving? _____

List the vitamins in the food. Give the percent (%) of the RDA in each serving.

_____

_____

_____

_____

_____

Is there any protein in a serving? Write *yes* or *no*.

_____

Is there any fat in a serving? Write *yes* or *no*.

_____

Are there any carbohydrates in a serving? Write *yes* or *no*.

_____

Looking at Nutrients

Now look at what you wrote about the two packaged foods. Write the answers to the next questions.

Which food (per serving) has more calories? _____

Does one food have more vitamins? If so, write its name.

_____   _____

Do you think one food has more nutrients than the other food? If so, write its name.

_____

Words for Consumers

Draw a line from each word on the left to its meaning on the right. The word meanings can be found in Chapter 5 of the *Consumer Skills for Teenagers* text. The first one is done for you.

ingredients	the amount of nutrients the government says a person needs every day
USDA	cloth made from chemicals
sodium	things people need to stay healthy
nutrients	the things which go into a good (such as food)
synthetic	a government agency that gives meat and other foods the "okay"
RDA	another name for salt

Now find the same words in the puzzle below. The words can be found by reading across, down, and from corner to corner. The first one is done for you.

```
M X R T Y L A A U Q X Z
B I N G R E D I E N T S
O S C T A P O L U U P O
F Y S A U C H Y M T I D
E N C H A S D N A R R I
N T N T R H D I S I R U
O H I I C T E A T E Y M
G E D N U O R S G N L T
P T A R D A R A O T T N
I I P T U L I V E S O O
A C Y U O K C O T O F U
```

More Words for Consumers

Look at the list of words. Use them to fill in the sentences below. You can find the words and their meanings in Chapter 5 of the text.

side effect   generic   warnings   care   natural

Down

1. To find what are the side effects of using some medicines, read the

_____ on the labels.

2. Labels tell consumers how to _____ for

clothing.

Across

3. Cloth that is made from plants or animals is called

_____ .

4. Sometimes medicines give people headaches. The headache is one

kind of _____ _____ .

5. Medicines which usually cost less than brand name medicines are

called _____ medicines.

Now use the above words and the directions to fill in the puzzle below.

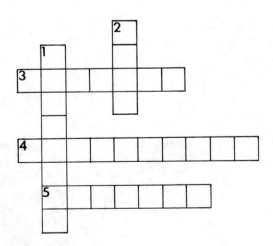

What Should You Look For on Clothing Labels?

For this activity you will need two pieces of your clothing. Each piece of clothing must have a label that tells what it is made of and how to care for it. If you can, pick one piece of clothing that looks and feels good to you. Name this "Number One." Pick one piece of clothing that does not look or feel as good. Name this "Number Two." Look at the labels on the clothing. Then fill in the table below.

	Number One	Number Two
What is the piece of clothing? (Write *dress, pants,* or whatever it is.)		
What is the clothing made of?		
Do you like the way it looks? (Write *yes* or *no.*)		
How should it be cared for? (Write the directions for care.)		
Do you think it is easy to care for? (Write *yes* or *no.*)		

Know Your Clothes

Now use the table on page 28 to answer the questions. Pick the best answer and fill in the lines.

Which is more important to you: clothing that looks good, or clothing that is easy to care for?

_____

looks good/easy to care for

Which piece of clothing is easier to care for?

_____

Number One/Number Two/both the same

Which piece of clothing looks or feels better?

_____

Number One/Number Two/both the same

Suppose you go shopping for clothes. You look at the labels on clothing you might buy. Of what cloth might you want the clothing to be made?

_____

same as Number One/same as Number Two/does not matter

Suppose you go shopping for clothes. You look at the labels on clothes you might buy. What directions for care would be best for you?

_____

same as Number One/same as Number Two/does not matter

6
More Ways to Check Quality

after page
36

Asking Friends About Quality

In Chapter 6, you read that there are many ways to find out about quality. Asking people you know is a good and easy way to find out about quality. But be careful. Your friends may have different ideas about quality than you do. This next activity may show this.

For this activity you will need two friends. Pick a food place at which you and these two friends have eaten. Ask the friends the questions in the table below. Tell them to answer *yes* or *no*. Then fill in the table with their answers. Write *yes* or *no* in each box.

	Person One	Person Two
Do you like to eat at _____? (Say the name of the food place.)		
Do you think most of the food there tastes good?		
Do you think the food is fresh?		
Is the service good?		
Would you tell other friends to eat there?		
Which food do you think is best?		

What Did You Learn?

Check (√) the sentence which tells best what your friends think about the food.

_____ My friends think the same things about the food.

_____ My friends think very different things about the food.

_____ My friends think more or less the same things about the food.

Check the sentence which tells best what your friends think about the service.

_____ My friends think the same things about the service.

_____ My friends think very different things about the service.

_____ My friends think more or less the same things about the service.

Now you answer the questions in the table. Then check the sentence below which tells best what you and your friends think. This is about the food place only.

_____ I think the same things my friends do about the food place.

_____ I think very different things than my friends do.

_____ I think more or less the same things as both of my friends.

_____ I think more or less the same things as one of my friends.

Ask Again

For this activity you will also need two friends. They can be the same friends that you asked about the food place. They can be different friends if you like.

Pick a movie theater that you and these friends have gone to. Then ask your friends the following questions. Tell them to answer *yes* or *no*. Then fill in the table with their answers. Write *yes* or *no* in each box.

	Person One	Person Two
Does the movie theater show mostly good movies?		
Is the sound good in the movie theater?		
Is the picture big enough there?		
Is the popcorn and candy always fresh?		
Is it ever too hot or too cold in there?		
Is there ever too much noise there?		
Would you take a friend to see a movie there?		

32

What Did You Learn?

Check (√) the sentence which tells best what your friends think about the movie theater.

_____ My friends think the same things about the movie theater.

_____ My friends think very different things about the movie theater.

_____ My friends think more or less the same things about the movie theater.

Answer the questions in the table. Then check the sentence which tells best what you and your friends think. This is about the movie theater only.

_____ I think the same things my friends do.

_____ I think very different things than my friends do.

_____ I think more or less the same things both of my friends think.

_____ I think more or less the same things one of my friends thinks.

Think about what you learned. Check the sentence that tells what you think about your friends and quality.

_____ Friends may tell me a lot about quality.

_____ Friends may not be good to ask about quality.

_____ Friends always have the same ideas as I do about quality.

Filling Out A Warranty Card

Many times when you buy a good you will get a special card with it. This card is a **registration card.** It helps make sure you get what your warranty promises. It shows when you bought the good. It shows how long your warranty lasts.

It is the consumer's job to fill out the card. It is the consumer's job to mail it. In this activity you will fill out the card for the camera.

Fill in Figure 4. Do the following steps. Use Figure 5 on page 35 to help you.

• Circle the words "Registration Card" on Figure 4.

• Fill in your name, address, city, state, zip code, and phone number.

• Fill in the line next to "Date Bought." This is the date you bought the camera. (Use today's date.)

• Fill in the line next to "Place Bought." This means the store where you bought the camera. Use the name "Smith's." Or use the name of a store in your town.

• Fill in the line next to "Model Number." Look at Figure 5 on page 35 of this book. The model number is on the front of the camera.

• Fill in the line next to "Serial Number." Find the words Serial No. on Figure 5. Then write the ten numbers that follow them. Make sure the numbers you write on the card match the numbers on the camera.

REGISTRATION CARD

Please fill out and return this card to make sure you get your warranty.

Name _____

Address _____

City _____ State _____ Zip Code _____

Date Bought _____ Place Bought _____

Model Number _____ Serial Number _____

Megaron, Inc.   2424 - 19th Street, Oakland, CA 94111

Figure 4. A Registration Card

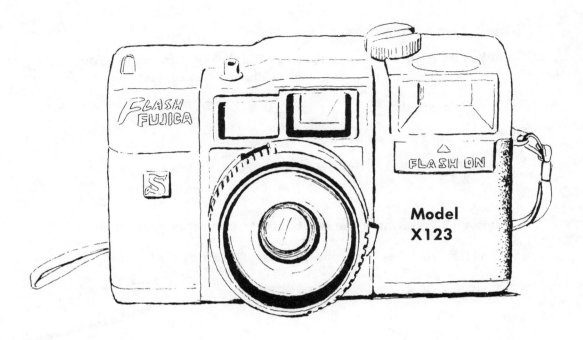

Front

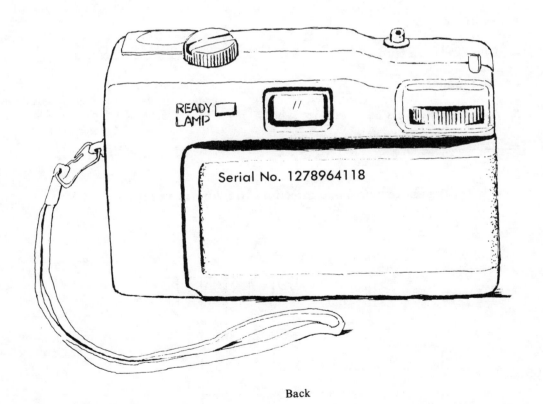

Back

Figure 5.   The Front and Back of a Camera

Words For Consumers

Look at the list of words. Use them to fill in the sentences below. You can find the words and their meanings in Chapter 6 of the text.

warranties   limited   labor   express   implied

Down

1. Another word for work done on a good or service is

_____ .

2. Almost all goods have warranties. These warranties promise that

goods will do what they are supposed to do. These are called

_____ warranties.

Across

3. A salesperson tells you a good will last for 21 days. He has made you a

special promise. He has given you an_____

warranty.

4. Two kinds of express_____are called

full and limited.

5. A warranty covers parts but not labor. This is a

_____warranty.

Now use the above words and directions to fill in the puzzle.

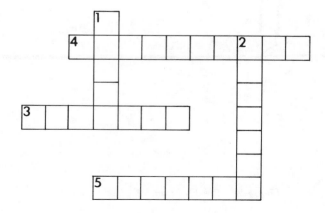

Using Consumer Magazines

Below is a story. It is from an imaginary magazine called *Consumer's Friend*. Read the story. Then answer the questions below.

A Look at Three Toothpastes

We looked at three brands of toothpastes. Then we looked at three things about each brand. We looked at whether each came in a tube or a pump. We looked at how much it would cost to use each toothpaste per month. (This was for two people brushing their teeth three times a day. We figured they would use 1/2 inch of toothpaste on their brush each time.) We looked to see if the toothpaste had flouride. Flouride helps keep teeth strong.

What we found out is in the table below.

Brands	Tube or Pump	Cost per Month	Flouride
Clean	pump	$.71	no
Smile	tube	.63	yes
Bright	pump	.85	yes

Consumer's Friend thinks that Smile toothpaste is the best buy. It has flouride. It costs less to use per month than the other brands. We do not think it is any harder to use a tube than a pump. Smile comes in a tube.

What Did You Read?

Write the answers on the lines below.

What amount of toothpaste does the story say each person might use each time he or she brushes?

_____

What is the toothpaste the story says consumers should use?

_____

Does Smile toothpaste have flouride?

_____

Suppose you do not like the taste of Smile. You want your toothpaste to have flouride. Which toothpaste would you buy, Clean or Bright?

_____

7
Getting a Good Price

after page
45

More on Unit Pricing

You read about unit pricing in the *Consumer Skills for Teenagers* text. The goods in Chapter 7 had signs which told you what each unit price was. What if there are no signs? You can figure out what the unit price is on your own. To find the unit price, do the following steps.

• Find the price of the good.

• Find the number of units in the good. This might be pounds, ounces, grams, and so on. It also might be the number of goods inside a package.

• Divide the price by the number of units.

This is the way to write the problem:

Price of Good ÷ Number of Units = Unit Price

The following problems will show you more about how to find the unit price.

Unit Price Problems

A bag of Washington apples weighs three pounds. A bag of Wolf River apples weighs four pounds. You want to see which bag costs less per pound. What unit will you be using?

_____

grams/ounces/pounds

The bag of Washington apples costs $1.50. To find the unit price of the apples, divide $1.50 by three. Why? Remember:

Price ($1.50) ÷ Number of Units (3) = Unit Price

Now do the problem.

$1.50 ÷ 3 = _____ .

$40.00/$.30/$.50

The bag of Washington apples costs $.50 per pound.

Now you must find what the bag of Wolf River apples costs per unit. A bag of Wolf River apples weighs four pounds. It costs $1.60.

Write your problem on the lines below. Then do the problem.

$ _____ ÷ _____ = _____
     Price   **Number of Units**   **Unit Price**

Now fill in the lines below using what you found.

The Washington apples cost _____ per unit,

or per pound. The Wolf River apples cost _____

per unit, or per pound. I will get more fruit per pound for my money by

buying the _____ apples.

      Washington/Wolf River

More Unit Price Problems

Suppose you go to a store to buy some paper. You do not care what the paper weighs. You want to get the most pieces of paper for your money. The unit you will be using in these problems is pieces of paper.

One package of paper has 60 pieces of paper in it. It costs $1.20. Write the problem below and find the unit price.

$ _____ ÷ _____ = _____
    Price   **Number of Units**   **Unit Price**

The second package of paper has 150 pieces. It costs $3.00. Write the problem and find the unit price.

$ _____ ÷ _____ = _____
    Price   **Number of Units**   **Unit Price**

The third package of paper costs $2.00. It has 200 pieces of paper in it. Write the problem and find the unit price.

$ _____ ÷ _____ = _____
    Price   **Number of Units**   **Unit Price**

Now fill in the lines below using what you found.

In the first package, each piece of paper cost _____.

In the second package, each piece cost _____.

In the third package, each piece cost _____.

I will get more pieces of paper for my money by buying the

_____ package.

first / second / third

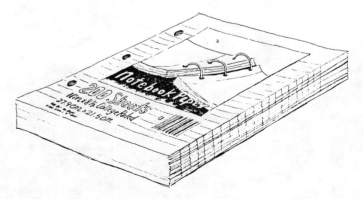

Do Generic Goods Have Lower Prices?

Do generic goods cost less than brand name goods? Find out on your own. Do the following steps.

Look at the packages in Figure 6 and 7 on this page. One package of paper cups is **generic.** It has no brand name. Which do you think is generic, the package in Figure 6 or Figure 7? Write the answer here.

_____

Find the unit price of the cups in Figure 6. The units you will be using are the number of cups instead of the weight. Why? You do not care about the weight of the cups. You care about how many cups are in each package. Write the problem below. Then do it.

$ _____ ÷ _____ = _____

    Price   **Number of Units**   **Unit Price**

Find the unit price of the cups in Figure 7. Write the problem. Then do it.

$ _____ ÷ _____ = _____

    Price   **Number of Units**   **Unit Price**

You are going on a picnic with your friends. You want to buy the most paper cups for your money. Will you buy the cups in Figure 6 or Figure 7? Write your answer here.

_____

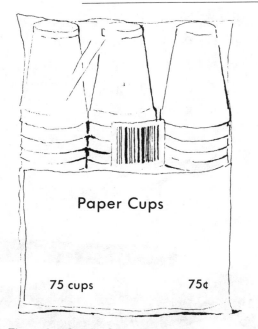

Figure 6.   One Package of Paper Cups

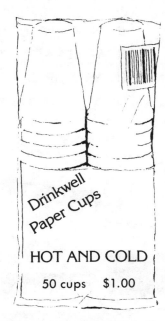

Figure 7.   A Second Package of Paper Cups

Words for Consumers

Draw a line from each word on the left to its meaning on the right. All the words can be found in Chapter 7 of the *Consumer Skills for Teenagers* text.

boutique   a time when stores lower the prices on goods

factory outlet   a small clothing store with high prices

department store   large store with many goods, prices usually less than a boutique's

sale   a place to buy clothes left over after boutiques and department stores buy what they want; prices are low

Now find the same words in the puzzle below. The words can be found by reading across, down, and from corner to corner.

```
A I S W D N N I T I S W L G C N T
A L N E T H E G D N E A E O E O Y
A C W O N E R B O U T I Q U E T H
A I H O S I E C R V E R A K P E N
L D E P A R T M E N T S T O R E O
E S O W L D L O V O I F Y N A E S
D N O W E O Y I A M D I O P N I B
R W H A T T O U G D O N A T C V T
H Y Z F A C T O R Y O U T L E T I
G N D D Q Y R N O I T I S X W A N
```

MUKAI DEPARTMENT STORE

8
Three Ways to Pay for Goods and Services

after page
56

Words for Consumers

Look at the list of words. Use them to fill in the sentences below. You can find the words and their meanings in Chapter 8 of the text.

cash   money order   layaway   credit   receipt

Down

1. Consumers can have a good put away for them. The consumers can then make payments on the good. They can buy the good on a

_____plan.

2. The part of the money order which you keep is called the

_____.

Across

3. If you do not want to carry cash, you can buy a _____

_____from a post office or a bank.

4. Dollar bills and coins are called_____.

5. You cannot pay for things with _____ until

you are 18 or older.

Now use the above words and the directions to fill in the puzzle.

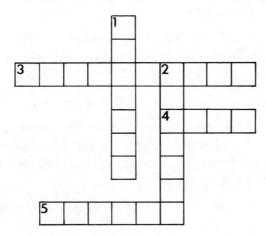

9
Consumer Rights and Resources

after page

58

How to Get What You Want

In this activity, you will practice an important skill. You will practice speaking in such a way that you will get what you want.

Below is a short play for you and a friend to read through aloud. Take the part of the consumer. Read the lines after you see the word "Consumer." Your friend should take the part of the salesperson. He or she will read the lines after the word "Salesperson."

As you read through the part of the consumer, remember to speak in a clear, even voice.

The Scratched Record

The consumer goes into a record store. He or she is carrying a record in its jacket. The consumer has a receipt.

Consumer: Hello. I bought this record from you yesterday. *(He shows the salesperson the receipt.)* I would like a new record in its place. This record was already scratched when I took it out of the jacket.

Salesperson: We don't take back records.

Consumer: Well, if the record was not scratched I wouldn't be bringing it back. I don't want my money back. I would like a new record in its place.

Salesperson: We don't take back records. Look kid, go play your games with somebody else.

Consumer: This record is new. It is not supposed to have any scratches. I would like to get a new one in its place. If you can't help me, let me speak to the person who runs the store.

The salesperson takes the record and looks at it.

Salesperson: How can you tell this record is scratched anyway? This guy sings like a frog. *(He laughs.)*

Consumer: The record was scratched before I played it. I was very careful when I took it out of the jacket. I would like to get a new record in its place.

Salesperson: How do I know you didn't scratch the record?

Consumer: I often buy records here. This is the first time I have had to bring a record back. I know that this store usually sells good records. This one was scratched before I got a chance to play it. I would like to get a new record.

Salesperson: Give me your receipt. Come back in a week or so. Maybe I can help you then.

> **Consumer:** If you cannot help me, let me talk to the person who runs the store.
>
> **Salesperson:** She's not here.
>
> **Consumer:** I will come back when she is here. What is your name?
>
> **Salesperson:** Look, I guess I can give you a new record. But it is almost quitting time for me. I have to get home. Why don't you come back tomorrow?
>
> **Consumer:** Maybe I should come back when the person who runs the store is here.
>
> **Salesperson:** Oh, well, come on. I'll give you a new one.
>
> **Consumer:** Thank you very much.

What did you do as the consumer? You did not give up. Sometimes you may need to say over and over again what you want. How many times did the consumer in this play say "I would like a new record in its place?" Count the number of sentences and write the number below.

_____

Ask your friend how he or she felt as the salesperson. Did it seem like the consumer was going to give up? Write whether your friend said *yes* or *no*.

after page

60

What Goes In a Letter?

Consumers may have to write a letter to take care of a problem. Figure 8 tells you what to put in a letter. Read through Figure 8. Pay attention to what goes in the letter. Notice where to put things, too. You do not have to write anything yet.

Your name
Your address
Your city, state, and zip code

Person you are writing to
Name of the company
Address
City, state, zip code

Dear _____ :
     fill in person's name

I am writing because I am unhappy with . . . (Write what you bought, where you bought it, and when you bought it.)

I am unhappy with it because . . . (Write why you are unhappy with what you bought.)

I would like (Write whether you want your money back, to return the good for a new one, and so on.) I am sending you a copy of the receipt.

I would like to hear from you in the next three weeks. If I don't I will let a consumer group in my city know about the problem.

Sincerely,

Your name

Figure 8.   Things to Write in a Letter

Now go on to page 47.

Now read through the sentences below.

You are writing to Thomas Mason, President, Wear It Right Clothing, at 6666 - 17th Street in Berkeley, California, 94111. You bought a Wear It Right sweater. You bought it from Bear Clothing in your city on February 5th of this year. The label on the sweater said to wash the sweater in warm water. You did this. The sweater became smaller. You want your money back. You talked to the person who runs Wear It Right, Mr. Jones. He would not give you your money back. Why? The sweater was on sale when you bought it.

You have made a copy of the receipt.

Write Your Own Letter

Write your own letter on the lines below. Use the information from the story above. Use Figure 8 on page 46 to help you. You can also use Figure 26 on pages 60-61 of the text.

Dear _____:

_____

_____

_____

_____

_____

_____

10
Using What You Know

You can put the skills you have learned to work when you buy almost anything. Imagine you are buying a used car. Which skills might you use?

Read the sentences below. Some of the sentences tell the ways you might use your skills when buying a car. Pick out those sentences and write them on the lines below.

I would read the want ads for used cars.

I would read consumer magazines to find out about the quality of the car.

I would get someone who knows about cars to look at it.

I would buy a car that would last only a few weeks.

I would ask my friends which cars they think have good quality.

I would buy the first car I saw without looking around.

I would buy a car with a good warranty.

I would buy a car that was too small for me.

I would buy a car without knowing anything about its quality.

Ways I Would Use My Skills

_____

_____

_____

_____

_____

_____

_____

_____

_____